BILBO'S LAST SONG

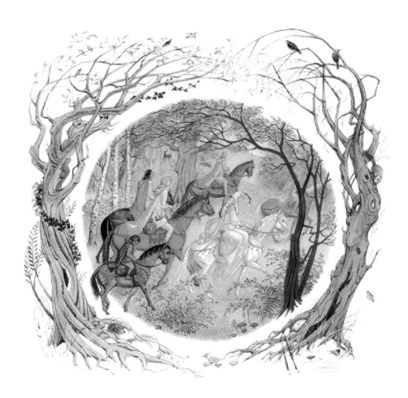

J.R.R. TOLKIEN

Illustrated by Pauline Baynes

BILBO'S LAST SONG
A RED FOX BOOK 978 0 099 43975 2
an imprint of Random House Children's Publishers UK
A Random House Group Company

First published in Great Britain by Unwin Hyman Ltd 1990
Hutchinson edition published 2002
This Red Fox edition published 2012

1 3 5 7 9 10 8 6 4 2

Red Fox Books are published by Random House Children's Publishers UK,
61–63 Uxbridge Road, London W5 5SA

www.**randomhousechildrens**.co.uk
www.**totallyrandombooks**.co.uk
www.**randomhouse**.co.uk

Addresses for companies within The Random House Group Limited can be found at: www.randomhouse.co.uk/offices.htm

THE RANDOM HOUSE GROUP Limited Reg. No. 954009

A CIP catalogue record for this book is available from the British Library.

Printed in China

The Random House Group Limited supports the Forest Stewardship Council® (FSC®), the leading international
forest certification organization. Our books carrying the FSC label are printed on FSC®-certified paper. FSC is the
only forest certification scheme endorsed by the leading environmental organizations, including Greenpeace.
Our paper procurement policy can be found at www.**randomhouse**.co.uk/environment.

MIX
Paper from
responsible sources
FSC® C104723

Day is ended, dim my eyes,
but journey long before me lies.

Farewell, friends! I hear the call.
The ship's beside the stony wall.

Foam is white and waves are grey;
beyond the sunset leads my way.

Foam is salt, the wind is free;
I hear the rising of the Sea.

Farewell, friends! The sails are set,
the wind is east, the moorings fret.

Shadows long before me lie,
beneath the ever-bending sky,

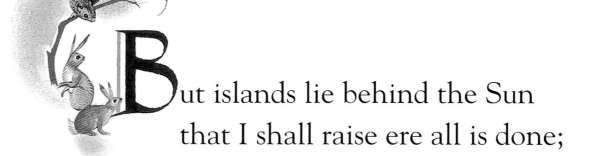

But islands lie behind the Sun
   that I shall raise ere all is done;

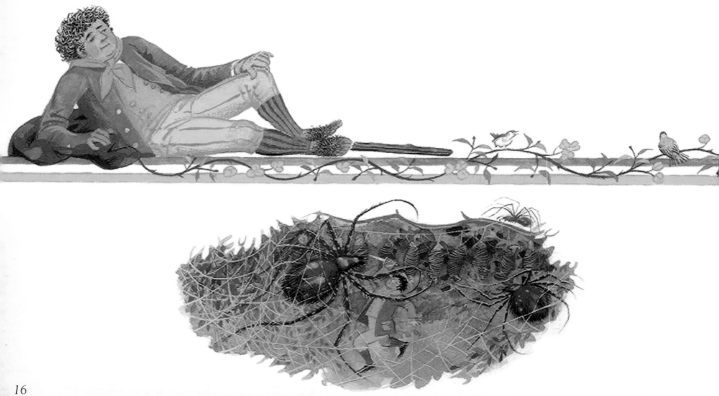

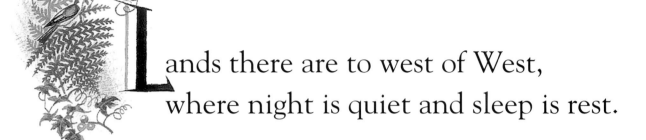

Lands there are to west of West,
where night is quiet and sleep is rest.

Guided by the Lonely Star,
beyond the utmost harbour-bar

I'll find the havens fair and free,
and beaches of the Starlit Sea.

Ship, my ship! I seek the West,
and fields and mountains ever blest.

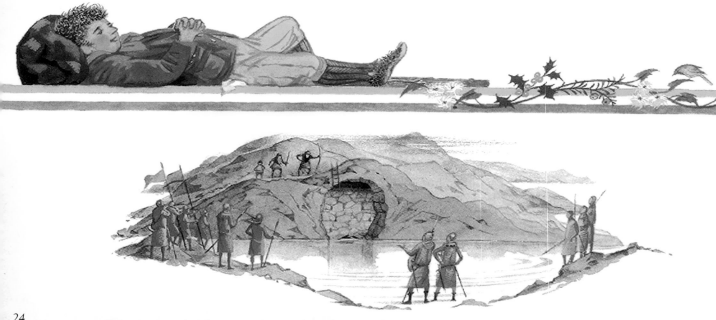

Farewell to Middle-earth at last,
I see the Star above your mast!

J. R. R. Tolkien was born in 1892 in Bloefontein, South Africa, but moved to England when he was small. After serving in the First World War, he became a distinguished professor at Oxford University. His first work of fiction, *The Hobbit*, was published in 1937 and his infamous epic, *The Lord of the Rings*, took him twelve years to write and was published in three volumes in the 1950s. He died at Oxford in 1973 at the age of eighty-one.

Pauline Baynes was born in Hove, Sussex, and studied at Farnham School of Art. As well as being Tolkien's favourite illustrator, she was also chosen by C. S. Lewis to illustrate the *Narnia* books. She illustrated more than 100 books during her lifetime.

BILBO'S LAST SONG
(at the Grey Havens)

Day is ended, dim my eyes,
but journey long before me lies.
Farewell, friends! I hear the call.
The ship's beside the stony wall.
Foam is white and waves are grey;
beyond the sunset leads my way.
Foam is salt, the wind is free;
I hear the rising of the Sea.

Farewell, friends! The sails are set,
the wind is east, the moorings fret.
Shadows long before me lie,
beneath the ever-bending sky,
but islands lie beneath the Sun
that I shall raise ere all is done;
lands there are to west of West,
where night is quiet and sleep is rest.

Guided by the Lonely Star,
beyond the utmost harbour-bar
I'll find the havens fair and free,
and beaches of the Starlit Sea.
Ship, my ship! I seek the West,
and fields and mountains ever blest.
Farewell to Middle-earth at last,
I see the Star above your mast!

J R R Tolkien.

NOTES ON THE PICTURES

The pictures in this book spring from two sources. The large paintings on the right-hand pages are based on episodes at the end of *The Lord of the Rings* (the specific volume is referred to by its initials), in which the Ring-bearers ride westwards to the Grey Havens, where they take ship for the Undying Lands. The narrative describes Frodo and Sam riding to meet a company including Bilbo, Elrond, Galadriel and Gildor, as well as many other elves. We may assume that this party had set out from Rivendell: Elrond had told Frodo two years before that he would soon depart. (ROTK, p. 267)

The poem that forms the text of this book is Bilbo's. Like Elrond, he had indicated to Frodo that his thoughts were turning towards departure. (ROTK, p. 266)

It therefore seemed right to think of the beginning of that last journey, and of Bilbo's part in it. The first four large pictures are thus based on a sequence of events which we can only imagine, but which must logically have occurred.

The smaller pictures, running at the bottom of both left- and right-hand pages, show scenes from *The Hobbit*. Bilbo (portrayed at the left-hand side of the page) remembers his first journey as he goes on his last journey.

1. There are several fleeting glimpses of Bilbo at Rivendell 'in his little room. It was littered with papers and pens and pencils'. (ROTK, p. 264)

i. 'A perfectly round door like a porthole, painted green, with a shiny yellow brass knob in the exact middle.' (H, p. 11)

ii. 'All that the unsuspecting Bilbo saw that morning was an old man with a staff.' (H, p. 13)

2. Bilbo looking out of his window, thinking about making his last journey. 'The window opened on to the gardens and looked south across the ravine of Bruinen.' (FOTR, p. 250)

i. 'Gandalf sat at the head of the party with the thirteen dwarves all round: and Bilbo sat on a stool at the fireside.' (H, p. 19)

ii. After his unexpected tea-party, Bilbo slept late the following morning. In consequence, he didn't get the dwarves' letter until half past ten – and had ten minutes to meet them at eleven o'clock at the Green Dragon Inn, Bywater. 'Bilbo could never remember how he found himself outside . . . running as fast as his furry feet could carry him.' (H, p. 33)

3. It was just as Frodo and the other hobbits left Rivendell to return to the Shire on 5th October 3019 (Shire Reckoning 1419) that Elrond said, 'About this time of year, when the leaves are gold before they fall, look for Bilbo in the woods of the Shire. I shall be with him.' (ROTK, p. 267) Bilbo and Elrond are here talking about that last journey. The ring Vilya, 'mightiest of the Three', with its sapphire stone, can be seen in Elrond's hand.

i. The first part of Bilbo's journey with the dwarves was merry, but once they had left the Shire the weather turned cold and wet. They came across 'dreary hills, rising higher and higher, dark with trees. On some of them were castles with an evil look, as if they had been built by wicked people.' (H, p. 34)

ii. '"Dawn take you all, and be stone to you!"' (H, p. 42) Tom, Bert and William (Bill) Huggins – the trolls – had captured the dwarves and Bilbo.

Gandalf had tricked them into arguing all night about the best way to cook their prisoners, until the sun rose and turned the trolls to stone. The trolls' cave where the swords Glamdring and Orcrist were discovered, and where Bilbo found the knife he later called *Sting*, is in the hill on the left.

4. 'With them went many Elves of the High Kindred who would no longer stay in Middle-earth.' (ROTK, p. 309) The elves who had decided to leave assemble at Rivendell. Galadriel is in the foreground on her white palfrey, with Bilbo on his grey pony.

i. The company with Elrond, when they rested at the Last Homely House for a while. The dwarves are (from the left): Ori (grey hood), Dwalin (dark green hood), Bifur (yellow hood), Gloin (white hood), Balin (red hood), Bofur (yellow hood, at the back), Fili (blue hood, fair hair), Bombur (pale green hood), Kili (blue hood, fair hair), Thorin Oakenshield (sky blue hood with a silver tassel, key on chain around neck), Oin (brown hood, at the back), Dori and Nori (purple hoods).

ii. 'One day they met a thunderstorm – more than a thunderstorm, a thunderbattle.' (H, p. 55)

5. 'Riding . . . behind on a small grey pony . . . was Bilbo himself.' (ROTK, p. 308) The ring Nenya, made of *mithril* with a white stone, can just be seen on Galadriel's hand.

i. 'Out jumped the goblins . . . and they were all grabbed.' (H, p. 58)

ii. 'Suddenly his hand met what felt like a tiny ring of cold metal lying on the floor of the tunnel.' (H, p. 65)

6. 22nd September 3021 (S.R. 1421): 'Frodo and Sam halted and sat silent in the soft shadows, until . . . the travellers came towards them.' (ROTK, p. 308) Frodo, riding Strider, and Sam, riding Bill, set out from Bag End on 21st September, and on the evening of 22nd joined the Last Riding of the Keepers of the Rings in Woody End. Frodo has a grey hood, Sam a red one.

i. 'Deep down here by the dark water lived old Gollum.' (H, p. 67)

ii. 'It was the trees at the bottom that saved them.' (H, p. 88) Having escaped from the goblins, and come out on the eastern side of the Misty Mountains, Bilbo and his friends are caught in a rock slide.

7. Dawn, 29th September 3021 (S.R. 1421): 'They came to the Far Downs . . . and looked on the distant Sea.' (ROTK, p. 310)

i. '"*Fifteen birds in five firtrees*"' (H, p. 94) The Lord of the Eagles comes to the rescue of the company: the flames from the goblins' fires can be seen in the reverse at the base of the trees. From the left, Fili and Kili have climbed a larch tree, Dori, Nori, Ori, Oin, Gloin and Bilbo are in a pine, and Bifur, Bofur, Bombur and Thorin are in another. Dwalin and Balin have taken refuge in a fir tree, and Gandalf is alone in a large pine tree.

ii. '"Who are you and what do you want?"' (H, p. 105) Beorn the skin-changer talks with Gandalf and Bilbo. His bees (bigger than hornets) and beehives are on the left, and his long low wooden house with two wings is in the background, with two of his horses.

8. 'As they came to the gates, Círdan the Shipwright came forth to greet them.' (ROTK, p. 310) Gandalf is behind Círdan, wearing the Ring of Fire, Narya the Great, with its red stone.

i. 'The idea came to him to lead the furious spiders further and further away from the dwarves.' (H, p. 138) It was in his first fight with the spiders of Mirkwood that Bilbo gave his sword the name *Sting*. It was a blade made thousands of years before in the hidden city of Gondolin.

ii. 'Long and searchingly he questioned the dwarves about their doings.' (H, p. 148) Thranduil, king of the Wood-elves, sits on his chair of carven wood in his halls lit with red torch-light, and he is crowned with berries and red leaves. Thorin had been captured earlier, and was imprisoned separately. Bilbo (invisible because he was wearing his ring) was never caught.

9. 'Then Círdan led them to the Havens, and there was a white ship lying.' (ROTK, p. 310) Elrond, holding a silver harp, is standing behind the hobbits.

i. 'First he unlocked Balin's door.' (H, p. 154) Bilbo found being invisible enabled him to track down the cells in which each dwarf was imprisoned. He was visible when he rescued them: the dwarves had to see who he was and be able to follow him.

ii. 'He found it quite as difficult to stick on as he had feared.' (H, p. 159) This picture is based on J.R.R. Tolkien's own colour painting of the barrels floating down the Forest River.

10. 'Up rode Merry and Pippin in great haste.' (ROTK, p. 310) Gandalf had sent them a message, so that they could say farewell, and so that Sam should not have to go home on his own.

i. 'They could see the Lonely Mountain towering grim and tall before them.' (H, p. 173) As Bilbo and the dwarves journeyed towards the Lonely Mountain (Mount Erebor) they stored some spare goods in a tent (extreme right of picture). The River Running rose out of the mountain and flowed out through the Front Gate.

ii. 'Stand by the grey stone when the thrush knocks, and the setting sun with the last night of Durin's Day will shine upon the key-hole.' (H, p. 52) The dwarves' New Year's Day was the first day of the last moon of Autumn on the threshold of Winter. When the moon and the sun were in the sky together it was called Durin's Day.

11. 'And the ship went out into the High Sea.' (ROTK, p. 310)

i. Bilbo, invisible because he is wearing the ring, steals a cup from Smaug's vast hoard – the dragon doesn't quite wake up. (H, pp. 184–5, 189)

ii. When Smaug attacked Esgaroth, he was fiercely resisted by the archers led by Bard. Smaug's fiery breath set light to the thatched roofs, and many people, including the Master, tried to escape in boats. Bard was told by the thrush of the one place – a hollow patch on the left breast – where Smaug was not armoured with jewels and gold embedded in his hide. (H, pp. 209–12)

12. Evening, 29th September, 3021. The End of the Third Age. 'Sam . . . saw a shadow on the waters that was soon lost in the West.' (ROTK, p. 311) The Ring-bearers depart, and from this moment the Fourth Age is dated.

i. 'The gate was blocked.' (H, p. 220) Faced by demands for compensation for damages from the men of Esgaroth, supported by their allies the Wood-elves, the dwarves fortified the Front Gate and altered the course of the stream to make a lake in front of it. Men and elves laid siege to the mountain.

ii. Attacked by goblins and wolves, the one-time foes – elves, men and dwarves – joined forces to fight the Battle of Five Armies. This picture shows the last phase of the battle, when the Eagles joined in.

13. '. . . white shores and beyond them a far green country under a swift sunrise.' (ROTK, p. 310) The white ship has sailed beyond the bent seas of Middle-earth, and reached the Undying Lands.

i. 'He would only take two small chests, one filled with silver, and the other with gold, such as one strong pony could carry. "That will be quite as much as I can manage," said he.' (H, p. 246) Bard would have rewarded Bilbo richly for all that he had done, but Bilbo would only accept a modest present. After many months of adventures, he was glad to be heading home in Gandalf's company.

ii. 'He was quite content.' (H, p. 254)